ANOTHER PAIR OF UNDERPANTS

ANOTHER PAIR OF UNDERPANTS

TONY HUSBAND

FOREWORD BY HARRY ENFIELD

INDEX

Published in 1995 by Index
by arrangement with Boxtree Ltd,
Broadwall House, 21 Broadwall, London SE1 9PL

First published in Great Britain in 1994 by
Boxtree Limited

10 9 8 7 6 5 4 3 2 1

ISBN 0 7522 1617 1

Cover design by Design 23

Printed and bound in Finland by WSOY

A CIP catalogue entry for this book is available from the British Library.

For Mum
with all my love
and with thanks for the gift of humour

"I said no rude words."

Tony Husband is older that you would think, taller than you would think, and wears a slightly put-upon expression. He talks in a hushed Northern accent with a permanently reverential air. Imagine a Sunday service in an impressive Northern church. There are rather more worshippers than usual, and the priest is about to give communion. The chief altar boy steps forward and quietly says to the priest "Father, I don't think there are quite enough hosts to go round". This is the tone in which Tony Husband talks all the time. His face betrays an air of worried bemusement at finding himself in the cut-throat world of satire. He seems resigned to the fact that the world is not as nice as he would like it to be. This unaggressive resignation is a feature of many of his cartoons in this book – wives resigned to the eccentricities of their husbands, owners resigned to the behaviour of their pets, parents resigned to the tastes of their children. This is a delightful collection and will appeal to anyone who, like me, feels that it's all over, so we might as well make do with what we've got.

HARRY ENFIELD, 1994

"I'm not criticising, Norman, but I just presumed the pond would be in the garden."

"This will get the neighbours talking."

"Can we come round? We're feeling at a bit of a loose end –
the tortoise is hibernating."

"Are you sure you've got the right angle on this fantasy football thing?"

"Sorry about this; my husband was brought up by wolves."

"I'm not happy with the way they've lifted my bum."

"Ah, Beddows, nice to see you, and this must be the little woman."

"OK, if I'm not fat, why do these tic birds mistake me for a hippo?"

"He'll ring you back – he's racing the pigeons."

"Charles, are you ashamed of me?"

"Since his retirement he's missed the cut and thrust of business."

"Can he ring you back? He's looking for his erogenous zones."

"Sorry, Jerry has a spittoon next to his chair at home."

"Oh, they have their own fish shop."

"It's very windy where we come from."

"Oh please don't leave dear how will I get on without you?"

"I'm your wife dammit! I've every right to know where you go at night."

"It's your mother. She wants a chat – have you got a spare three hours?"

"OK, which of you bastards had the last After Eight?"

"Bad day at the office, dear?"

"My husband's a night watchman."

"Oh darling, do you mean it, you want to marry me?"

"You'll have to excuse my wife, her period is due."

"My husband has got a new hobby – counting pollen."

"You're a man of the world, Milnthorpe. It's my wife's birthday –
what underwear does she like?"

"Oi, do you find me (a) very sexy, (b) sexy, or (c) not very sexy at all?"

"To save all that getting to know me crap, here's a video of my life so far."

"Don't be fooled by Gordon's demeanour –
animal sexual lust bubbles just under the surface."

"For the last time, we're not buying you any headphones."

"Sit still now. Daddy made this video for you before he went to work."

"I'd best go – he wants his dinner."

"How do you spell 'pathetic'?"

"It's because he's a garden gnome, isn't it?"

"Have you got your donor card with you, just in case?"

"He takes his football viewing very seriously."

"Heads we do it, tails we don't."

"For God's sake, if you can't sleep, read a book or something!"

"We're nearly there, Matthews, the first men ever to conquer the North Peak."

"I think we've sacrificed too much for this child."

"He's trained the cat to hide his bald patch."

"For heaven's sake, Nigel, he'll talk when he's ready."

"I'm more of a bottom man myself."

"You should involve your wife more in your sport. I did –
Maggie's turning into a damn fine caddie."

"OK Julie, you've proved you can do it, now will you shave it off."

"Mum, I think Grandad has fallen in the piranha tank."

"My son was saying you go like a rabbit."

"Oh don't worry – I'm used to turbulence. I've been married for twenty years."

"Mum, look at this rocket I found under your bed."

"Stop being so dramatic, Barry. It's only an overdue library book."

"You're the first invisible friend I've ever had."

"I never seem to know what you're really thinking these days, Amanda."

"Oh, don't get me wrong. I adore sex. It's just sex with him I can't stand."

"Frank, the Xpelair is playing up again."

"Of course, we're pleased you've taken up tennis son, it's just. . ."

"What do you mean, will I sex you up?"

"It's my wife, Doctor. She seems very tense."

"Rodney, this is Tracey. You'll like her, she's boring too."

"Joe's really busy. He's having to bring work home with him every night."

"We're fascinated by your escapology hobby, Brian,
but you've been in there three hours."

"Why don't we buy a car?"

"We're saving up for one of those papoose carriers."

"No, he wasn't at the birth. Why should he be? He wasn't at the conception."

"OK, the loser does the pots."

"James, sort out your sock drawer, and be ruthless!"

"This your first swap party too?"

"It says bald men are more virile. Well, I suppose there's always the exception."

"YooHoo, it's Mum and Dad. We've let ourselves in."

"Brian, what exactly did you put in that letter to the prime minister?"

"I'll be glad when the TV's repaired."

"Right, who wants to see a video of Joyce and me having sex?"

"Phew, not bad for couple of old gits."

"Ignore Randolph. It's his way of telling me the central heating's on too high."

"What's this about you and some circus clown?"

"Stop it Thomas, every time Mother calls!"

"I don't care how dirty they get on television."

"I think we've had enough sex for one marriage, don't you Humphrey?"

"You'd have thought the doctor would come out."

"Er, Duncan, you seem to have the wrong idea about wife-swapping."

"The dog's my darling little Trixie. The man's my husband."

"It's so much better now. We used to have an outside loo."

"It's Meryl Streep. She wants to know if she can play you in a new Hollywood blockbuster."

"Can't you just go for a swim like everyone else?"

"OK, who's for Scrabble?"

"My wife's having an affair. I'll kill him when I find out who he is."

"Henry's making a quilt for Bosnia from his old underpants."

"You spoil that cat."

"Apparently they're friends of your father's from the golf club."

"God, has anyone ever told you you've got a stupid grin?"

"We're hoping one day to afford the balloon."

"Yeah, I'll give you a tip – stop looking down my wife's dress!"

"What's gone wrong between us, Duncan?"

"If only he'd give me a sign of his true feelings."

"I tell you that bird hates me!"

"When are you going to tell your father his dog's dead?"

"I christen you. . .oops."

"Seems my husband is rather smitten by your breasts."

"Do you have to wear your cap every time?"

"But we don't want to play statues."

"His passion for potato men started when we found out we couldn't have children."

"I wonder if we'll get invited to eat at the captain's table."

"Yes, our marriage is going through a rough patch."

"When you've finished house training the dog, dinner's ready."

"Hey up, it's the Paris fashion show – don't you want to watch it?"

"I suppose you're wondering about my sexual prowess?"

"Miss Fodham's here for your piano lesson, so where have you hidden the piano?"

"Look, we're not shouting, just tell us where you've buried Grandad."

"Stop whinging. I save a fortune buying in bulk."

"Son, tell us straight – you're not taking hallucinogenic drugs, are you?"

"You don't seem as uptight with this period, darling."

"According to the adverts those underpants are supposed to give you a feeling of power."

"Dear Tom Cruise, I'm often mistaken for you. . ."

"I said no, Timothy. I'm too old to take up the trapeze."

"I think he wants walkies."

"We'll go in the back room – it's Roger's parachute training class tonight."

"Helen, can we cancel tonight? Philip's just spontaneously combusted."

"If I had a favourite, it would have to be Terence the Digger."

"It's been a very nice evening, but could you go now? We want to have sex."